Under His Father's Wing

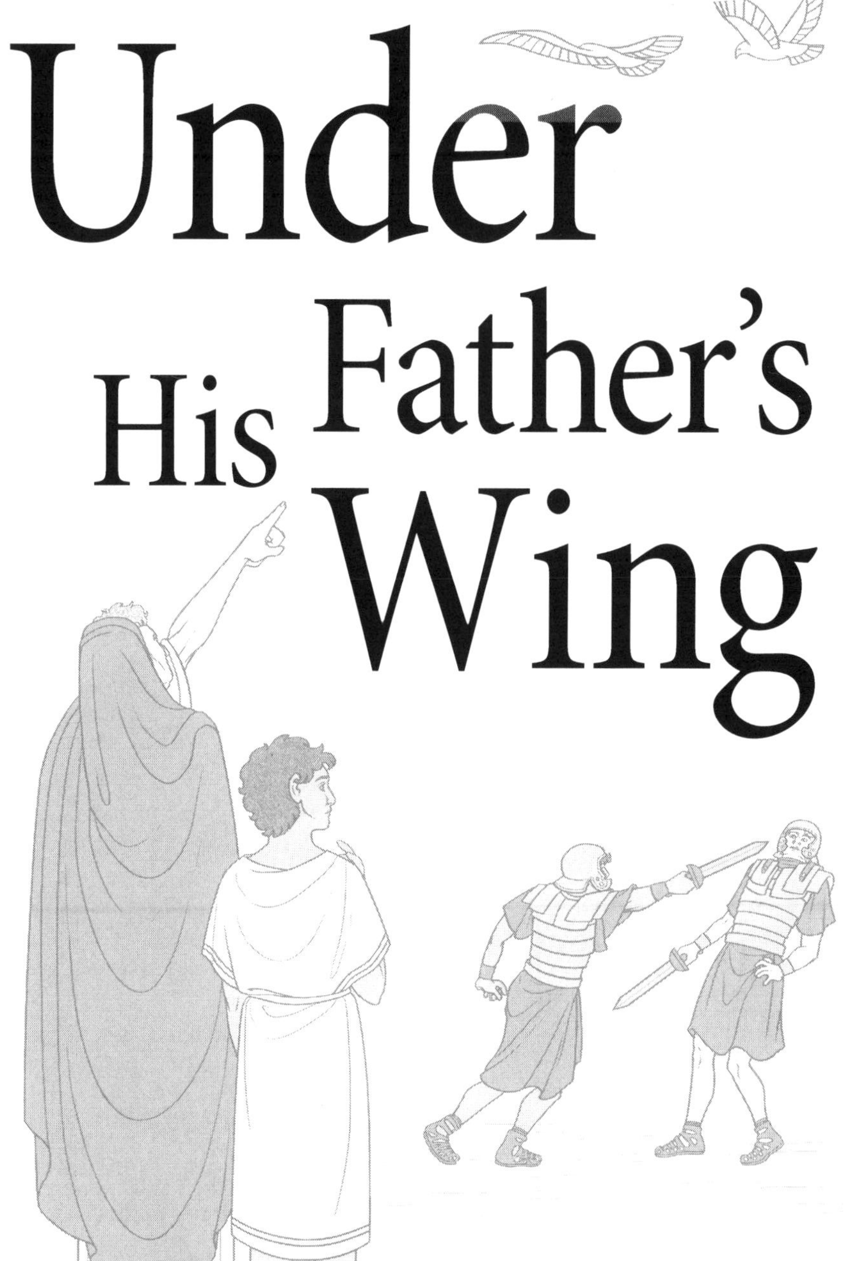

Encounter Latin

Series Information

The *Encounter Latin* novella series is designed to engage and delight novice and intermediate Latin learners with comprehensible stories written entirely in Latin. Focusing on a range of subjects related to antiquity, these books feature limited, high-frequency vocabulary alongside ample illustrations and other text supports. Each novella in the series is grouped by topic; within a given topic, novellas progress step-by-step in language complexity across four different levels while building on established concepts and vocabulary. The four levels correspond to the following guidelines:

- Level A (green cover): 100–150 unique Latin words
- Level B (blue cover): 150–200 unique Latin words
- Level C (red cover): 200–250 unique Latin words
- Level D (purple cover): 250+ unique Latin words

Ideal for independent reading or to introduce aspects of ancient culture in the classroom, each novella in the *Encounter Latin* series can be read as a stand-alone text or alongside other levels as part of a more extensive exploration of a given topic. The *Encounter Latin* novellas also coordinate with the nonfiction pre-readers in the *Explore Latin* series. For more information and updates, check our website: www.BOLCHAZY.com.

Encounter Latin

Under His Father's Wing

Mārcus dē Auguribus Discit

Emma Vanderpool

Introduction by Robert Patrick

Illustrations by Lucrezia Diana

Bolchazy-Carducci Publishers, Inc.

Wauconda, Illinois USA

Editor: Amelia Wallace
Introduction: Robert Patrick
Illustrations: Lucrezia Diana
Design & Layout: Adam Phillip Velez
Cover Illustration: Eagle from a thirteenth-century Franco-Flemish bestiary (Digital image courtesy of the Getty's Open Content Program).

Under His Father's Wing
Mārcus dē Auguribus Discit

Emma Vanderpool

Bolchazy-Carducci Publishers, Inc.
1000 Brown Street
Wauconda, Illinois 60084
www.bolchazy.com

Printed in the United States of America
2021
by Publishers' Graphics

ISBN 978-0-86516-876-3

Library of Congress Control Number: 2021940458

Contents

Preface

This novella is a continuation of the first in the series, *Augury Is for the Birds*, whose prior reading is merely encouraged and not necessary to understand the book currently in your hands. *Under His Father's Wing: Marcus de Auguribus Discit* totals about 2,600 words and contains 159 unique Latin words (excluding proper nouns such as personal names). About one-third of its vocabulary, primarily the theme-specific vocabulary, occurs in *Augury Is for the Birds.*

This novella continues a conversation between Marcus, a Roman boy who dreams of being a heroic soldier, and his father Titus, who wants his son to learn the art of augury, much to his son's dismay. They explore the importance of augury and its role in historical, political, and military contexts by looking at examples from Homer's *Iliad* as well as moments in early Roman history (as described in Livy's *Ab Urbe Condita*).

While the first book in the series focuses more on the specific mechanics of augury and bird flight, this book explores how military and political leaders used augury to make decisions and how it could be seen as a source of authority and power. Examinations of war are colored by both Marcus's romanticization of fighting and his father's trauma resulting from his experiences as a Roman soldier. While these stories aren't necessarily new, the tension between these two realities helps to complicate the viewpoint encapsulated in Horace's famous line, *dulce et decorum est pro patria mori* ("it is sweet and fitting to die for one's country"). I hope that this novella can serve as a starting point for valuable classroom discussions concerning duty to country and duty to family.

I owe the highest of thanks to my tireless editor for the press, Amelia Wallace, who was unwaveringly patient with me as we worked through this story together, and to my two anonymous readers, who offered valuable feedback on the earliest drafts. Dr. Robert Patrick carefully reviewed the text and wrote a generous introduction. This book would not be the same without Sarah Penso and Forrester Hammer, who read with careful attention to both narrative and Latinity; any remaining errors are mine alone. Matthew Katsenes and the students of Moultonborough Academy offered valuable classroom feedback.

I gratefully dedicate this book to my parents, Diane and Dale, for their belief and support in this and all my wildest projects and aspirations.

Emma Vanderpool
Springfield, MA

Introduction

In the last five years, the field of teaching Latin has experienced a phenomenon new to this modern period of teaching: novellas. The more than seventy novellas published recently attest to a new kind of focus in teaching and learning the Latin language: the goal, with noted effects, of putting in front of students stories that are understandable at their current level of work and contain content that they find engaging, we might even say, alluring. Writers of these novellas have aimed their work at every level of student from the absolute beginner to those who have three to five years of study behind them. And the effects? Students develop the ability to actually read and understand Latin stories through Latin itself without the need or burden of attempting to translate in order to understand. Through the efficacy of understandable and engaging stories, students have almost from the beginning the experience of the language in the language itself.

Out of the earliest conversations about the *Encounter Latin* novellas, the publisher and the authors made a most valuable commitment to four things that have become the framework of the series. These commitments are to work within a limited, high-frequency vocabulary, to align the novellas with the reading proficiency guidelines of the American Council on the Teaching of Foreign Languages (ACTFL), to write these stories in a way that is comprehensible to readers within a given proficiency level, and to create stories that students of the twenty-first century might find compelling. To that end, authors are making use of the Dickinson College Core Latin vocabulary, which is a high-frequency list (top one thousand) of Latin words found in authors of the classical period. I cannot state strongly enough how important it is for Latin teachers to familiarize themselves with the ACTFL reading proficiency descriptions for the Novice and Intermediate levels (which are the levels attainable in a four-year program). Each level is subdivided into low, mid, and high ranges, creating six gradations of reading proficiency. The word "intermediate" has been used in varying ways over the decades by Latin teachers, often without any firm basis for what each has meant by it. The ACTFL guides clearly articulate what students can do at each of the six gradations of proficiency. The novellas in this series are framed by those articulations. It is important to note that these novellas do not follow any sort of a grammar syllabus. With the commitment to a limited vocabulary and writing that is comprehensible at the indicated proficiency level, authors have been free to use whatever grammar is needed to tell a compelling story. This may seem difficult to some teachers at first, but strikingly, when this approach is used, students do not find it difficult, and that is the primary focus.

The novella that you hold in your hands, *Under His Father's Wing* by Emma Vanderpool, is what the publisher is calling their Level B novella. Vanderpool limited this novella to 159 unique words with a total text of just over 2,600 words. Vanderpool crafted this novella, as the Level B indicates, for the Novice Mid to Novice High reading proficiency. A reader at this reading proficiency level will be able to recognize high-frequency words in a context that strongly supports those words used both singly and in short phrases and sentences. In this Level B novella, in fact, in the very first chapter, the reader will encounter what teachers know to be indirect statements. Because they are written with vocabulary that is supported by context (and has been previously established in the Level A book), with only minor supports from the teacher, students will navigate these indirect statements with little difficulty.

A novice reader requires a great deal of repetition, which supports meaning, and may be helped by the use of true cognates. The use of cognates is, however, a bit of a gamble since it depends largely on the reader's first language. My own experience is that students whose first language is Spanish or Romanian (with strong communities of both in my region of the country) recognize true cognates far more quickly than speakers of English. Teachers of Latin who have been using the ALIRA Latin Reading Proficiency test (co-produced by the American Classical League and ACTFL and based on the reading proficiency guides) find that students consistently score at the Novice Mid to High range by the end of the first year of Latin in US programs where students meet daily for Latin. That gives a helpful marker for this novella: it is appropriate for use in the latter part of the first year of Latin (and beyond).

Vanderpool has not only written a novella within these parameters of vocabulary and proficiency, but she has risen to the challenge of writing in a way that is both consistent with classical Latin and is understandable to students in this proficiency range. Vanderpool has written about augury and war within both Greek and Roman contexts, mixing the two ancient cultures in ways that feel authentic by using the particular powers of storytelling. This is no lecture on Greco-Roman culture and history. It is a story, but as a story it invites the reader into multiple landscapes, times, settings, and relationships. Hopefully, readers will lose themselves and forget for a moment that they live in another time and that they are reading in another language. We call this experience "getting into the flow," and when that happens, all kinds of reading magic are possible. When "the flow" happens, language acquisition increases with what seems like no effort, and in this case, the rich culture and history that we love to lecture about has been delivered in a way that students simply will not forget. To the contrary, they very likely will emerge from the novella eager to have more conversations about this thing called augury, ancient war making, and the interpenetration of two world cultures, with all the connections that we are able to make to these concepts for our time.

This novella and those in the *Encounter Latin* series can be used in a number of ways. While space here does not allow for even an outline of potential lesson plans, I am happy to suggest four potential uses and three examples of what that may look like in a Latin classroom.

1. **Sustained Silent Reading (SSR):** We know that there are two forms of input that enable learners to acquire a new language: listening and reading. While both of those are necessary for students to make progress, reading is slightly more effective than listening. Regardless of the rest of the shape and design of a Latin program, having regularly scheduled periods of SSR with material that is appropriate (with vocabulary that is 90–95 percent known by students; comprehensible and compelling) is a real boost for student progress in the language. Teachers may plan SSR on almost any schedule, once a week, twice a week, for a portion of a period (helpful especially on block schedules), or for an entire class period. Whatever plan a teacher chooses, SSR in a Latin classroom provides time for students to read Latin stories at the appropriate level independently. This independent reading enriches and supports all the other work that students may do in collaboration with their teacher and deeply enhances the effects of the novella mentioned above.

   Another variation of SSR is the degree to which the teacher gives students choice in their reading. There may be local constraints on how much material a teacher can provide for choice, but the appeal of material that is not only understandable but also engaging is enhanced when students have choice. This form of SSR where students may choose between a number of appropriate level novellas is often referred to as FVR—free, voluntary reading. When appropriate material is introduced for this independent period of reading, and students come to expect that it is a regular part of their Latin learning, they will settle into the routine and even complain if it is, for whatever reason, interrupted.

2. **Enrichment and Differentiation:** How individual teachers conceive of enrichment and differentiation will depend largely on how the rest of their program is framed. The times will still come, however, in which they need and want materials to put into the hands of students who are ready for something more. Very often we forget that "something more" can simply mean something different. Teachers can become frustrated when they see that some in their class seem to pick things up very quickly and grow bored or that some students seem to be bored all the time while lagging behind. Putting the appropriate level novella in their hands can be the "something different" that they need. Enrichment can look like what some students do while others receive remediation or receive extra time for assessments. Differentiation can look like a variety of things that we ask a student to do with a novella. It could be to read two pages and consider how the artwork involved reflects what they have read. It could be to read an entire chapter and imagine how the next chapter unfolds. It could be to draw additional artwork for a chapter. In the best sense of differentiation, it may well look like all of those things happening at once in the same classroom.

3. **Supplementation:** For this use of the novella, I have in mind that regardless of what else drives and frames one's Latin program, a novella of appropriate material can

become some of the variety that the human brain craves. Latin programs are framed and driven by textbooks, by themes, by grammar syllabuses, by the adapted works of chosen authors, and by established vocabulary lists. A novella can be used to break up what otherwise becomes the monotony of the program—whatever that is. What I have in mind by supplementation is not, "if we finish the textbook (or units, or district curriculum), we will read a novella." I mean interrupting whatever that program is in order to read the novella. And I don't mean interrupt the program until the novella is finished but rather use the novella as an unexpected surprise, variety for the brain, interspersed all through the year.

4. **Curriculum Content:** It is becoming more common for Latin teachers to abandon textbooks (for a variety of reasons). As they look to high-frequency vocabulary lists and themes that allow them to work with all of the national standards (Communication, Culture, Connections, Comparisons, and Community), they would do well to consider making novellas appropriate to the level a featured part of what they do. These novellas have made the commitment to high-frequency vocabulary. They are written creatively in order to be compelling to students in the twenty-first century, and they engage the reader in the culture and history of classical Rome with a deep sensitivity to the multicultural reality of ancient Rome that our materials for far too long have ignored.

For the last two possibilities, supplementation and curriculum content, I will suggest, in briefest form, three ways that teachers may structure the use of this novella. We should think of these as three approaches to novella usage in addition to SSR. In other words, a teacher may have established times for SSR. Beyond that, the teacher may plan lessons in the following three ways, and these three approaches are not exclusive of one another. In fact, it is my common practice to make use of all three at all levels of Latin.

1. **Read and Draw:** This is a slow, introductory approach to the story in which the teacher and students read the story aloud together. They take small "bites" of the text together and then in one way or another create drawings to illustrate what they have read and understood. The drawings can be done in several ways: with whiteboards and markers, paper and pencil, computerized devices and drawing software, individually or in groups (one person drawing and the others suggesting details). Drawings may be labeled with Latin words and phrases from the story, given captions taken from the story, or both. An entire chapter can be turned into a four-, six-, or eight-frame cartoon. An entire chapter can be turned into a one-scene drawing that attempts to capture all the detail of the chapter. The Read and Draw approach can be made as short or as long (lasting several days) as the teacher determines is useful to student progress.

2. **Read and Discuss:** As a follow-up to Read and Draw, or without it depending on the needs of students, the teacher and students read portions of a story/chapter together and then in Latin have simple conversations about what they have just read. At lower proficiency levels, those questions can be yes/no questions and questions that explore basic details: *quis?, quid?, ubi?* As students seem ready, one may venture with the word *cur?* and its natural response *quod.* It is in the middle of such Read and Discuss sessions that teachers will see an ideal moment arise in which they may extend the material of the storyline into the personal stories of students. At that moment, the discussion becomes

Personal Questions and Answers—still kept at the right level for the proficiency. Perhaps the class has just read the following about a character: *Marcus miles esse volebat et in bello pugnare volebat*. Before turning to the historical and cultural issues of the book, the teacher might ask several students in turn, *Quid vis esse?* After a few rounds and replies (even if the answers are in English), the teacher might continue: *Discipuli, Janise vult esse medica. Quid Janise vult agere? Janise vult dormire? Currere? Homines adiuvare?* The simple inquiry into what a student wants to be allows the teacher to create some new language with nouns and verbs that students may not yet know through the enticing prospect of talking about themselves. (NB: Creating some feminine forms of words that might not exist in classical Latin is important to make it clear that doctors, teachers, and auto mechanics can be jobs that anyone is drawn to. That is a major feature of personalizing conversation in a language—it is only personal if it describes the people in the room). It does not matter that these words for modern jobs are not in the students' current vocabulary list. They will be drawn to the opportunity to speak about themselves before going on with a description of the character in the book.

3. **Read and Write:** When and only when students seem to have a strong grasp of a chapter or segment of a novella, it is appropriate to ask them to write about it in Latin (noting that writing in a second language always lags behind the reading proficiency). At lower proficiency levels, the writing can be a simple summary. Teachers can give students time to write, in Latin, about the characters and events of the appointed segment of the story. The time may be limited or not, but I find that students at all levels do better at this when they do not feel the pressure

> of time (so what may seem to the teacher as a ten to fifteen minute task may go much better for everyone in the room if they are given thirty minutes to do it, without announcing the time frame). In any regard, Read and Write is an approach to take at the end of a process, not at the beginning. It is most fruitful when the teacher has a sense that everyone is truly understanding the reading and has engaged with it already through drawings and class discussion. What to do with the writings (as in assessment) is a full and long consideration that we cannot do here, but suffice it to say that this writing does not require the teacher's scrutiny for error correction, but can be a helpful way of checking in to see that students are understanding what they are reading.

I am pleased to be able to introduce this second of several novellas in the B-C series that will only enhance and enrich the material through comprehensible and compelling novellas that Latin teachers have to draw on—novellas that did not exist even five years ago. These are not novellas that simply recast or adapt ancient authors. The authors who are creating them are seeking to invite the two worlds—ancient and modern—to see each other and to value the full scope of humanity that has always been there but has not always been seen or heard. If these novellas contribute more fully to that conversation, as I think they will, then there has never been a better time to teach and learn Latin.

Robert Patrick, PhD
March 30, 2021

Vocabulary Tree

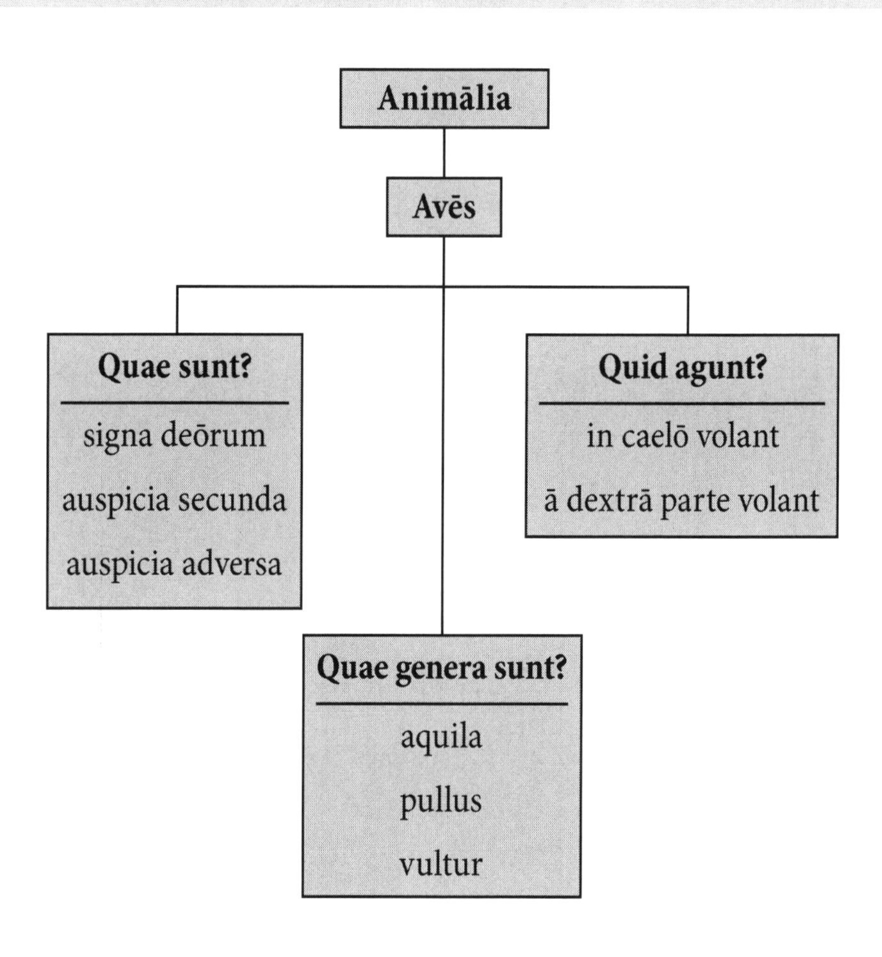

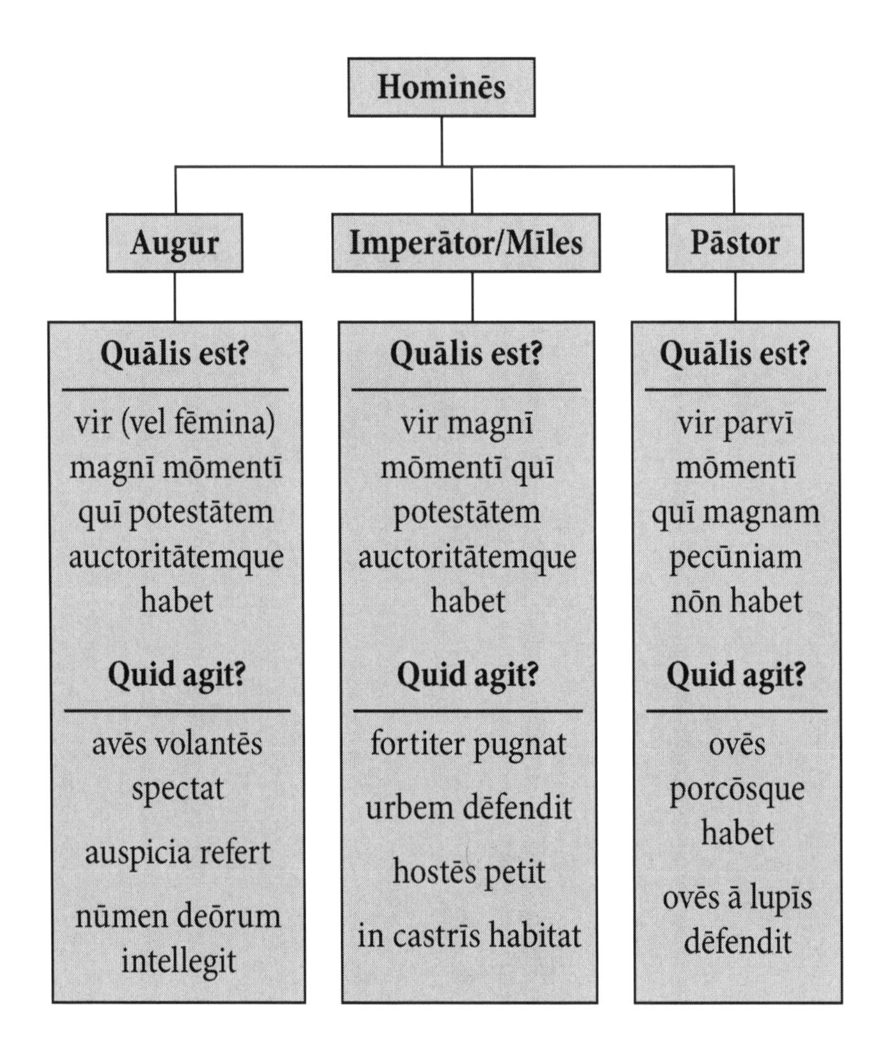
Hominēs
Augur
Imperātor/Mīles
Pāstor
Quālis est?
vir (vel fēmina) magnī mōmentī quī potestātem auctoritātemque habet
Quid agit?
avēs volantēs spectat
auspicia refert
nūmen deōrum intellegit
Quālis est?
vir magnī mōmentī quī potestātem auctoritātemque habet
Quid agit?
fortiter pugnat
urbem dēfendit
hostēs petit
in castrīs habitat
Quālis est?
vir parvī mōmentī quī magnam pecūniam nōn habet
Quid agit?
ovēs porcōsque habet
ovēs ā lupīs dēfendit

Persōnae

Pater et Fīlius

Mārcus, *fīlius, quī augur esse nōn vult*

Titus, *pater et mīles, quī fābulās dē auguribus narrat*

Bellum Trōiānum

Trōiānī

Hector, *imperātor*

Priamus, *rēx*

Aenēās, *imperātor*

Helenus, *augur et mīles*

Cassandra, *sacerdōs*

Graecī

Agamemnōn, *imperātor*

Achilles, *imperātor*

Ulixēs, *imperātor*

Calchās, *augur*

Rōmānī

Rōmulus et Remus, *frātrēs et pāstōrēs*

Ancus Mārcius, *quārtus rēx Rōmae*

Tarquinius Prīscus, *quīntus rēx Rōmae*

Tanaquil, *uxor Prīscī et augur*

Attus Navius, *augur rēgis*

Lūcius Papīrius Cursor, *imperātor*

Prologus

Ōlim erat fīlius mīlitis, nōmine Mārcus. Mārcus et magister Lūcius avēs in caelō volantēs spectābant. Lūcius augur nōtus et callidus erat, sed Mārcus augur esse nōlēbat. Mārcus mīles esse volēbat et in bellō pugnāre volēbat. Quamquam Mārcus mīles esse volēbat, pater Titus eum augurem esse volēbat. Titus multās fābulās dē auguribus et mīlitibus narrābat. Erant fābulae dē virīs Graecīs et Trōiānīs fortibus. Erant fābulae dē Rōmānīs callidīs. Pater volēbat fīlium intellegere *potestātem auctōritātemque* augurum.

---

potestātem auctoritātemque: power and authority

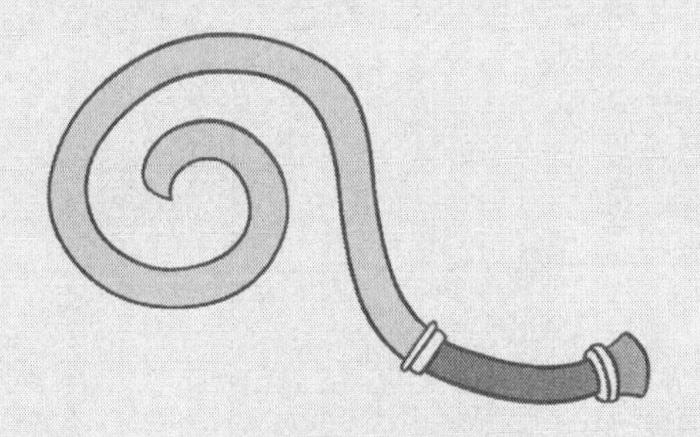

I. Fābulae dē Auguribus

Mihi nōmen est Mārcus. Meus pater Titus mē augurem esse vult. Pater crēdit augurēs esse virōs nōtōs. Rectē dīcit, sed augur esse nōlō. Mīles esse volō. Pater vult mē habēre *potestātem auctōritātemque.* Intellegō meum patrem mē amāre. Quamquam ego patrem amō, nōlō esse augur, quī avēs in caelō spectat.

"Pater," inquam, "mīles similis tibi esse volō. Multās fābulās dē tē audīvī. Tē Rōmam et rem pūblicam dēfendisse audīvī. Et familiam tuam ab hostibus dēfendēbās et populum Rōmānum.

---

potestātem auctōritātemque: power and authority

Mīlitēs virī nōtissimī et *maximī mōmentī* sunt quod rem pūblicam ab hostibus dēfendunt. *Bellum gerere* contrā hostēs difficile est. Hoc intellegō.

"Ego et magister meus avēs in caelō *volantēs* spectāvimus. In castrīs tē et amīcōs tuōs quoque spectāvī. Quamquam *auspicia* imperātōrī nōn *refers*, tū es mīles nōtus, cui omnēs pārent!"

"Rectē dīxistī," pater respondet. "Mē in castrīs spectāvistī sed mē bellum gerentem nōn spectāvistī. Mē in bellō *pugnantem* nōn spectāvistī. Bellum gerere horribile et difficile est. Necāre etiam hostēs difficile est.

---

maximī mōmentī: of the greatest importance
Bellum gerere: To wage war
volantēs: flying (describes *avēs*)
auspicia . . . refers: you report the omens
bellum gerentem: waging war (describes *mē*)
pugnantem: fighting (describes *mē*)

"Nostrī patrēs virī nōtī nōn erant. Et augurēs et mīlitēs *potestātem auctōritātemque* habent. Virī *maximī mōmentī* sunt. Rem pūblicam ab hostibus dēfendunt. Familiās dēfendunt. Imperātōrēs quī multum dē auspiciīs sciunt victōrēs in bellō sunt. Nōtissimī sunt. Fābulās dē hīs virīs tibi narrāre volō."

---

potestātem auctōritātemque: power and authority
maximī mōmentī: of the greatest importance

II. Mīlitēs Īliadis

"Homērus," pater inquit, "fābulās, Īliadem et Odyssēam, narrāvit. In hīs fābulīs erant multī augurēs nōtī. In bellō Trōiānō, Graecī contrā Trōiānōs pugnābant quod Helenam petēbant. Helena uxor imperātōris Graecī erat, quam Trōiānus Paris cēperat.

"Agamemnōn imperātor Graecus erat. Agamemnōn Hectorem timēbat quod Hector fortissimus Trōiānus erat. Agamemnōn signum ā rēge deōrum petīvit. Iuppiter imperātōrem audīvit et signum secundum mīsit.

Subitō in caelō Agamemnōn aquilam *hinnuleum tenentem* vīdit. Agamemnōn intellēxit aquilam esse avem Iovis et hinnuleum similem Trōiānīs esse. Hoc signum erat secundum: Iuppiter Graecōs in bellō victōrēs esse volēbat. Quod Agamemnōn et imperātor fortis et augur callidus erat, *nūmen* deōrum intellēxit. *Auspicium* secundum *referre* mīlitibus poterat.

---

hinnuleum tenentem: holding a fawn (describes *aquilam*)
nūmen: divine will
auspicium . . . referre: to report the omen

Auspiciīs relātīs, Graecī nōn iam timēbant et contrā Trōiānōs fortiter pugnāvērunt. *Iove volente*, Graecī victōrēs erant."

"Graecī," inquam, "Trōiānōs necāvērunt et victōrēs erant!"

"Rectē dīxistī," pater respondet. "In hōc bellō, Graecī multōs hostēs necāvērunt, sed multī Graecī quoque mortuī sunt. *Bellum gerere* difficile est. Dēfendere familiam ab hostibus difficile est.

"In hōc bellō, Iuppiter multa signa dedit. Rēx deōrum et Graecīs et Trōiānīs signa dedit. Priamus erat et rēx Trōiānōrum et pater; Hector fīlius fortis erat. Hector contrā Achillem pugnāvit, sed Achilles fortior quam Hector erat. *Trōiānīs spectantibus*, Achilles, fortissimus Graecōrum, Hectorem necāvit. Achilles mortuum mīlitem ad castra *retulit*.

Auspiciīs relātīs: When the omens had been reported
Iove volente: With Jupiter willing
Bellum gerere: To wage war
Trōiānīs spectantibus: While the Trojans were watching
retulit: (he) brought back

"Priamus fīlium ad urbem *referre* volēbat quod fīlium amāvit. Prīmum, rēx signum petīvit. Subitō ā dextrā parte, aquila per caelum volāvit. Laetus Priamus crēdidit signum secundum esse quod intellēxit aquilam avem Iovis esse. Priamus ad castra Graecōrum *iter fēcit* quod mortuum fīlium ad urbem Trōiam referre voluit. Achilles rēgem nōn necāvit, sed fīlium patrī dedit. *Iove volente*, Priamus fīlium ad urbem retulit.

"Mārce, mī fīlī, tū es fortis et callidus. Vīs esse mīles in bellō. Vīs dēfendere rem pūblicam ab hostibus. Intellegō. Ego quoque haec facere volō. Quamquam tē *potestātem auctōritātemque* habēre volō, Priamus esse nōlō. Tē, fīlium mortuum, ad urbem referre nōlō.

"Rēx deōrum multa signa Trōiānīs et Graecīs mīsit. Necesse erat omnibus signa rectē intellegere.

---

referre: to bring back
iter fēcit: (he) made a journey
Iove volente: With Jupiter willing
potestātem auctōritātemque: power and authority

Ubi mīlitēs avēs in caelō *volantēs* intellēxērunt, deinde victōrēs erant. Imperātōrēs quī bonī augurēs erant *bellum* bene *gessērunt.* Nōn multī mīlitēs mortuī sunt. Mīlitēs quōrum imperātōrēs auspicia nōn intellēxērunt mortuī sunt.

"Multī ex meīs amīcīs in bellō mortuī sunt. Quamquam rem pūblicam et familiās suās dēfendērunt, tamen mortuī sunt. Rōma urbs maxima est quod nōs fortiter pugnāvimus. Mīlitēs pugnant et pugnant et pugnant. Sed, mī fīlī, amīcōs *morientēs* vidēre difficile est. Horribile est. Difficillimum est tenēre amīcōs morientēs quod nihil facere potes."

---

volantēs: flying (describes *avēs*)
bellum . . . gessērunt: (they) waged war
morientēs: dying (describes *amīcōs*)

III. Augurēs Īliadis

"Necesse est pugnāre et rem pūblicam dēfendere," ego patrī meō respondeō. "Erit bellum. Mīlitēs in bellō pugnābunt et morientur. Hoc audīvī: '*dulce et decōrum est prō patriā morī*.'"

"Virī," pater inquit, "in bellō morientur. Quod tū augur callidus eris, nōn multī morientur. Et signa intellegere et *nūminī pārēre* est *maximī mōmentī*. Haec facere est rem pūblicam dēfendere."

"Homērus," inquam, "optimās fābulās narrāvit. In Īliade, multī mīlitēs et imperātōrēs erant augurēs. Mīlitēs avēs spectāre et *auspicia referre* poterant. Ego volō esse similis Agamemnōnī. Ego et mīles et augur esse volō."

---

dulce et decōrum est prō patriā morī: it is sweet and fitting to die for one's country (Horace, *Odes* III.2.13)

nūminī pārēre: to obey the divine will

maximī mōmentī: of the greatest importance

auspicia referre: to report the omens

"In bellō, nōn omnēs augurēs sunt mīlitēs," Titus respondet, "sed omnēs augurēs sunt virī *magnī mōmentī*. Calchās optimus augur Graecōrum et vir maximī mōmentī erat. Quod Calchās *nūmen* deōrum bene intellēxit, sciēbat *quid fuisset, quid esset, et quid futūrum esset.*

"Ulixēs imperātor callidissimus Graecōrum erat. Scīvit *iter* ad Trōiam *facere* difficile esse. Scīvit *bellum gerere* contrā Trōiānōs difficillimum esse. Trōiānī mīlitēs fortēs et callidī erant. Ulixēs igitur optimum augurum habēre volēbat. Augurem quī signa deōrum intellegēbat habēre volēbat. Calchāntem petīvit quod audīverat eum optimum esse augurem.

---

magnī mōmentī: of great importance

nūmen: divine will

quid fuisset, quid esset, et quid futūrum esset: what had been, what was, and what would be

iter . . . facere: to make a journey

bellum gerere: to wage war

"Ōlim Calchās serpentem novem avēs *cōnsūmentem* vīdit. Deinde serpēns saxum factus est! Calchās, augur callidus, intellēxit serpentem signum esse. *Auspicium* imperātōrī Ulixī *retulit*.

---

cōnsūmentem: eating (describes *serpentem*)
Auspicium . . . retulit: He reported the omen

Quod novem avēs vīderat, necesse erat multōs annōs *bellum gerere.* Ego bellum duōs annōs gessī. Hoc difficile erat. Pugnāre, igitur, multōs annōs difficillimum Graecīs erat.

"Omnēs—etiam Ulixēs—Calchāntem spectābant et eī pārēbant. Omnēs pāruērunt virō quī *auspicia* imperātōrī *retulit* quod deōs timēbant. Quamquam neque imperātor neque mīles erat, Calchās magnam *auctōritātem* habēbat.

"In castrīs Graecōrum, Calchās optimus et nōtissimus augur erat. In castrīs Trōiānōrum, Helenus optimus erat. Helenus fīlius rēgis Priamī et frāter Cassandrae erat. Quamquam Trōiānī Cassandrae nōn crēdēbant, omnēs Helenō crēdēbant. Helenus scīvit *quid fuisset, quid esset, et quid futūrum esset.*

---

bellum gerere: to wage war
auspicia . . . retulit: (he) reported the omens
auctōritātem: authority
quid fuisset, esset, et futūrum esset: what had been, what was, and what would be

"Ōlim neque Hector neque mīles Trōiānus Aenēās contrā Graecōs pugnāre volēbat quod multī Trōiānī in bellō moriēbantur. *Bellum gerere* contrā Graecōs difficile erat. Helenus nōn timēbat quod *nūmen* deōrum intellēxit. Scīvit Trōiānōs victōrēs futūrōs esse. Quod augur pugnāre voluit, imperātorēs et mīlitēs nōn iam timēbant sed fortiter pugnābant. *Dīs volentibus*, Trōiānī victōrēs erant."

"Intellegō," inquam. "Calchās mīles nōn erat sed *auctōritātem* magnam habēbat. Hector, optimus mīles Trōiānōrum, Helenō pāruit. Sed Helenus et augur et mīles erat! Et avēs in caelō *volantēs* spectābat et fortiter pugnābat. Quod Helenus cum mīlitibus pugnābat, bellum intellegēbat. Quod Helenus et mīles et augur erat, omnēs eī crēdēbant. Helenus mīles *maximī mōmentī* erat."

"Quod Helenus cum mīlitibus pugnābat, bellum intellēxit," pater respondet. "Intellēxit auspicia maximī mōmentī esse."

Bellum gerere: To wage war
nūmen: divine will
Dīs volentibus: With the gods willing
auctōritātem: authority
volantēs: flying (describes *avēs*)
maximī mōmentī: of the greatest importance

IV. Rōmulus et Remus

"Nunc volō," pater inquit, "narrāre fābulās dē virīs quī prīmum nōn magnam pecūniam habuērunt. Virī nōtī nōn erant. Deinde *potestātem auctōritātemque* habēre poterant quod augurēs erant.

"Ōlim erant pāstōrēs, quī prope septem collēs habitābant. Hī pāstōrēs ovēs habēbant et ovēs ā lupīs dēfendēbant. Virī nōn magnī mōmentī erant quod magnam pecūniam nōn habēbant. Pecūniam habēre est auctōritātem habēre. Prope collēs erat urbs Alba Longa. Virī quī in urbe habitābant magnam pecūniam habēbant.

---

potestātem auctōritātemque: power and authority

"Duo ē pāstōribus erant frātrēs similēs mīlitibus. Fortēs erant et familiam dēfendēbant. Et ovēs ā lupīs dēfendēbant et pāstōrēs ā hostibus. Hī frātrēs erant Rōmulus et Remus. Rōmulus et Remus pāstōrēs nōn magnī mōmentī erant. (Magnī mōmentī ovibus erant . . . .) Quamquam Rōmulus fīlius pāstōris erat, prīmus rēx Rōmae factus est.

"Rōmulus et Remus urbem suam aedificāre volēbant. Rōmulus prope collem Palātīnum urbem aedificāre voluit, Remus prope collem Aventīnum. Rōmulus nōmen 'Rōmam' urbī dare voluit, Remus 'Remoram.' Frātrēs voluērunt avēs in caelō spectāre et *auspicia* aliīs pāstōribus *referre*. Necesse erat frātribus avēs spectāre et auspicia referre quod necesse erat omnibus intellegere *nūmen* deōrum.

---

auspicia . . . referre: to report the omens
nūmen: divine will

"Collem Palātīnum Rōmulus tenuit, collem Aventīnum Remus. Aliī pāstōrēs Rōmulum rēgem habēre volēbant. Aliī frātrem eius rēgem esse volēbant. Omnēs pāstōrēs et caelum et frātrēs spectāvērunt.

"Prīmum Remus sex vulturēs in caelō vīdit. Quod Remus prīmum vulturēs vīdit, crēdidit sē rēgem esse. Laetus Remus auspicium virīs retulit. Pāstōrēs quī Remum rēgem esse voluērunt laetī erant. Signum secundum esse crēdidērunt.

"In caelō Rōmulus nōn sex vulturēs vīdit sed duodecim. Rōmulus intellēxit signum secundum esse. Laetissimus auspicium frātrī referēbat. Subitō duodecim avēs per caelum iterum volābant! Quamquam prīmum Remus sex vulturēs vīderat, omnēs crēdidērunt hoc signum secundius esse. *Signō vīsō*, Rōmulus rēx factus est et urbem, nōmine Rōmam, prope collem Palātīnum aedificāvit.

Signō vīsō: After the sign was seen

"Referre auspicia difficile est. Estne auspicium secundum? Estne adversum? Intellegere *nūmen* est habēre potestātem magnam. Intellegisne hoc, fīlī mī? Deī signum mīsērunt et omnēs nūminī pāruērunt. Rōmulus nōn iam erat pāstor *parvī mōmentī.* Nunc rēx maximī mōmentī erat. Quod Rōmulus augur callidus erat, nōmen urbī nostrae est Rōma, nōn Remora!"

Ego respondeō, "Rōmulus erat augur, quī auspicia referre poterat. Erat quoque mīles, quī bellum gessit et bene pugnāre poterat. Quod et augur et mīles erat, rēx nōtissimus factus est. In multīs bellīs pugnāvit et victor erat. Similis Rōmulō esse volō. Et auspicia referre et in bellīs pugnāre volō."

---

nūmen: divine will
parvī mōmentī: of little importance

V. Tarquinius Prīscus

"Rōmulus," pater inquit, "quī suum nōmen urbī dedit, augur erat. Postquam Rōmulus mortuus est, erant sex aliī rēgēs, *quōrum* multī augurēs erant.

"Ōlim vir Ētrūscus, nōmine Tarquinius Prīscus, cum uxōre *iter Rōmam faciēbat*. Quamquam magnam pecūniam habēbat, potestātem nōn habuit quod pater eius Graecus erat. Tanaquil, uxor eius, *virum parvī mōmentī* habēre nōlēbat. Quod Tanaquil Prīscum virum maximī mōmentī facere volēbat, iter Rōmam faciēbant.

---

quōrum: of whom, of which
iter Rōmam faciēbat: (he) was making the journey to Rome
virum: husband
parvī mōmentī: of little importance

"Tanaquil augur callida erat, quae avēs in caelō spectābat et nūmen deōrum intellegēbat. Prīscus et Tanaquil, *iter Rōmam facientēs*, aquilam vīdērunt. Subitō aquila ā dextrā parte *volāns pilleum* Prīscī cēpit. Avis pilleum *tenēns* per caelum volāvit. Deinde ad eōs volāvit et pilleum ad Prīscum *retulit*.

"Tanaquil signum intellēxit et auspicium retulit. 'Auspicium,' Tanaquil laeta inquit, 'secundum est. Secundum est quod aquila ā dextrā parte volāvit. Secundum est quod aquila avis Iovis est. Rēx deōrum signum mīsit. Pilleum, quī similis *corōnae* est, tibi dedit. *Iove volente*, tū rēx Rōmae eris!'

---

iter Rōmam facientēs: making the journey to Rome (describes *Prīscus et Tanaquil*)

volāns: flying (describes *aquila*)

pilleum: hat

tenēns: holding (describes *avis*)

retulit: (it) brought back

corōnae: to a crown

Iove volente: With Jupiter willing

"Laetissimī Tanaquil et Prīscus—cum pilleō—*iter Rōmam fēcērunt.* In urbe Rōmā, Prīscus vir nōtus erat quod callidus erat et magnam pecūniam habēbat. Ubi rēx Ancus Mārcius mortuus est, Prīscus rēx factus est quia uxor fābulam dē aquilā narrāvit. Nunc vir habuit et pecūniam magnam et potestātem auctōritātemque magnam.

"Aquila quam Tanaquil et Prīscus in itinere vīderant auspicium secundum fuerat. Quamquam Tarquinius Prīscus potestātem in Ētrūriā habēre nōn poterat, nunc potestātem auctōritātemque habēbat. Rēx erat! Tarquinius Prīscus vir maximī mōmentī nōn fuerat, sed rēx factus est quod Tanaquil augur callida erat. Nūmen Iovis rectē intellegere potuit. Quod Tanaquil auspicium omnibus retulerat, omnēs crēdēbant Iovem signum mīsisse. Tanaquil *virum* maximī mōmentī habēre voluerat et igitur, *signō vīsō*, Prīscum rēgem facere poterat.

---

iter Rōmam fēcērunt: (they) made the journey to Rome
virum: husband
signō vīsō: after the sign was seen

"Prīscus multa facere et aedificāre volēbat. Prīscus multa bella gessit in quibus Rōmānī victōrēs erant. Quod Circum Maximum et Cloācam Maximam aedificāvit, Prīscus urbem meliōrem fēcit.

"Bellum gerere et multum aedificāre difficile erat. Ubi rēgēs bellum gerēbant et multa aedificābant, intellegere nūmen deōrum magnī mōmentī erat. Callidus Prīscus hoc intellegēbat. Volēbat habēre augurem optimum, quī auspicia rectē referre poterat. Habēre augurem optimum erat maximī mōmentī rēgī. Tanaquil augur rēgis esse nōlēbat. Omnēs dīcēbant Attum Navium augurem optimum esse. Prīscus igitur Attum augurem rēgis esse voluit."

"Quis Attus Navius est?" inquam. "Nōtissimus vir nōn est!"

"Nōtus tibi nōn est," Titus respondet, "sed vir nōtissimus est!"

VI. Attus Navius

"Attus Navius," pater inquit, "pāstor erat quī nōn ovēs habēbat sed porcōs. Quod pāstōrēs magnam pecūniam nōn habēbant, neque auctōritātem neque potestātem habēbant.

"Ōlim Attus Navius porcum vidēre nōn iam poterat et igitur per collēs porcum in vīnētō petēbat. Callidus vir signum ā deīs petīvit. Deī sciēbant *ubi porcus fuisset, esset, et futūrus esset.* 'Deī,' Attus inquit, 'ubi est meus porcus? Date mihi signum et ego vōbīs optimās *ūvās* dābō!"

---

ubi porcus fuisset, esset, et futūrus esset: where the pig had been, was, and would be

ūvās: grapes

"Subitō Attus Navius porcum in vīnētō vīdit; laetissimus erat quod, *dīs volentibus*, nunc porcum habuit. Deinde necesse erat Attō dare *ūvās* optimās deīs. In tribus partibus vīnētī, avēs signa adversa fēcērunt. Pars in quā avēs signum secundum dedērunt ūvās optimās habēbat. Laetus Attus ūvās optimās deīs dedit.

"'Ō deī,' Attus inquit, 'quod signum mihi dedistis et porcum meum dedistis, vōbīs ūvās optimās dō.'

"Quamquam Attus pāstor *parvī mōmentī* fuerat, deī eum augurem nōtissimum fēcērunt. Nōn necesse eī erat bellum gerere. Nōn mīles erat sed potestātem auctōritātemque habēbat. Omnēs Rōmānī volēbant eum caelum spectāre et auspicia referre. Ubi Prīscus dē Attō audīvit, eum augurem rēgis fēcit.

"Ōlim Attus Navius magnam pecūniam nōn habēbat. Erat pāstor, quī porcōs habuit. Quod signa deōrum intellegere poterat, augur rēgis factus est. Nunc urbem ab hostibus dēfendēbat. Nōtissimus augur factus est. Vir maximī mōmentī factus est.

---

dīs volentibus: with the gods willing

ūvās: grapes

parvī mōmentī: of little importance

"Mārce, intellegisne? Attus nōn iam pastor *parvī mōmentī* erat. Augur maximī mōmentī factus est. Augurēs potestātem auctōritātemque habēre possunt; Rōmam ab hostibus dēfendere possunt. Augurēs virī nōtissimī esse possunt."

"Intellegō, mī pater," respondeō. "Similēs rēgī Prīscō, patrēs nostrī neque potestātem neque auctōritātem magnam habuērunt. Nōn erant virī maximī mōmentī. Similēs Attō, nōn magnam pecūniam habēmus. Augur esse possum, quī auspicia rectē refert. Potestātem auctōritātemque habēbō. Omnēs mē audient et mihi crēdent. Augur esse possum . . . sed nōlō.

"In bellō augurēs virī maximī mōmentī sunt. Sed ego volō esse mīles. Ego volō pugnāre contrā hostēs et rem pūblicam dēfendere."

"Intellegō," pater respondet, "sed fābulam dē imperātōre narrāre volō. Esse mīles est difficile; necesse est auguribus auspicia referre. Necesse est auguribus mīlitēs ab hostibus dēfendere."

---

parvī mōmentī: of little importance

VII. Lūcius Papīrius Cursor

"Auspicia rectē referre maximī mōmentī est," Titus inquit. "Audīvistīne fābulam dē imperātōre Lūciō Papīriō Cursōre? Papīrius imperātor fortissimus erat et potestātem auctōritātemque magnam habuit. In multīs bellīs pugnāvit et victor erat. Nunc Rōmānī gerēbant bellum contrā Samnītēs. Samnītēs hostēs Rōmānōrum erant.

"Ad urbem Aquilōniam imperātor iter faciēbat. Quod multī Samnītēs in urbe habitābant, Papīrius cum multīs mīlitibus iter faciēbat. Samnītēs in bellō fortissimī erant sed Rōmānōs timēbant.

"*Multīs fābulīs* dē bellō cum Samnītibus *audītīs*, mīlitēs Rōmānī fortiter pugnāre volēbant. Prīmum Papīrius pullārium petēbat. Pullāriī augurēs sunt quī signa pullōrum intellegunt. Pullāriī cibum pullīs dant. Necesse est pullīs multum cibum cōnsūmere. *Cibō cōnsūmptō*, pullārius dīcit deōs signum secundum dare. Imperātōrēs igitur facere possunt id quod volunt. Cibō nōn cōnsūmptō, pullārius dīcit deōs signum adversum dare. Imperātor igitur nihil facere potest. Mīlitēs pugnāre nōn possunt.

"Papīrius contrā Samnītēs pugnāre voluit. Necesse erat imperātōrī habēre signum secundum. Pullārius timēbat quod omnēs pugnāre volēbant. Et imperātor et mīlitēs pugnāre volēbant quod Samnītēs prope castra erant. Pullārius *timēns* auspicium nōn rectē retulit. Pullōs cibum cōnsūmpsisse dīxit . . . sed pullī cibum nōn cōnsūmpserant. Quamquam deī signum adversum dedērunt, pullārius auspicium nōn rectē retulit.

Multīs fābulīs . . . audītīs: Since they had heard many stories
Cibō consumptō: After the food has been eaten
timēns: fearing (describes *pullārius*)

"Pullārius auctōritātem habuit. Imperātor igitur eī crēdidit et Samnītēs *petere* voluit. Aliī pullāriī, quī in castrīs erant, timēbant. Scīvērunt auspicium adversum fuisse. Scīvērunt pullārium auspicium rēctē nōn retulisse. Papīrius audīvit id quod pullāriī dē signō adversō dīcēbant. Papīrius valdē timēbat quia numinī nōn rectē pāruit. Ubi mīlitēs Rōmānī intellēxērunt auspicium fuisse adversum, valdē timēbant. Quod pullārius auspicia rectē nōn retulit, Papīrius pullārium prīmum ad pugnam mīsit."

---

petere: to attack

"Ego," inquam, "volō esse similis pullāriō! Nōn bellum timeō! Nōn hostēs timeō. Imperātor mē ad pugnam prīmum mittet et—"

"Et *moriēris*, Mārce," pater respondet. "Papīrius pullārium prīmum ad pugnam mīsit quia auspicium nōn rectē retulit. Ubi augurēs auspicium non rectē referunt, multī mīlitēs moriuntur."

---

moriēris: you will die

VIII. Et Augur et Mīles

"Necesse est auguribus," inquam, "auspicia rectē referre. *Hōc factō*, rem pūblicam dēfendere possumus! Hoc maximī mōmentī est."

"Rectē dīxistī," Titus respondet. "Pullārius imperātōrem timuit. Quod auspicium nōn rectē retulit, mortuus est. Samnītēs eum necāvērunt. Postquam pullārius mortuus est, avis magna ā dextrā parte volāvit. Papīrius avem *volantem* spectāvit et nōn iam timēbat. Quamquam augur callidus nōn erat, auspicium secundum intellēxit. *Signō vīsō*, Rōmānī nōn iam timēbant sed fortiter pugnāvērunt. Difficile erat, sed Rōmānī victōrēs erant."

Hōc factō: When this has been done
volantem: flying (describes *avem*)
Signō vīsō: After the sign was seen

"Intellegō," inquam. "Necesse est imperātōribus augurēs audīre. Est maximī mōmentī auspicia rectē referre et signa deōrum rectē intellegere."

"Rectē dīxistī," Titus respondet. "Sciō tē mīlitem esse velle. Sciō tē similem mihi esse velle.

Vīdī tē *spectantem* nōn caelum sed mē in castrīs *pugnantem*. Timeō. Ubi mīles eram, virōs *bellum gerentēs* vīdī; bellum difficile et horribile est. Multī mīlitēs mortuī sunt; multī ex amīcīs meīs mortuī sunt. Mihi crēde. Bellum horribile est. Tū es fīlius meus. Quamquam '*dulce et decōrum est prō patriā morī*,' nōlō tē in bellō morī.

"Quod tē victōrem in bellō esse volō, necesse est tibi signa avium scīre et auspicia intellegere. Nōlō tē et tuōs amīcōs morī quod signa deōrum nōn intellēxistī.

"Volō tē callidum esse. Volō tē spectāre avēs in caelō *volantēs*. Volō tē signa deōrum intellegere et auspicia rectē referre. Volō tē esse et augurem et mīlitem nōtissimum. Deinde potestātem auctōritātemque habēbis. Deinde victor in bellīs eris et ego pater laetus erō."

---

spectantem: watching (describes *tē*)
pugnantem: fighting (describes *mē*)
bellum gerentēs: waging war (describes *virōs*)
dulce et decorum est prō patriā morī: it is sweet and fitting to die for one's country (Horace, *Odes* III.2.13)
volantēs: flying (describes *avēs*)

Grammatica

Superlative Adjectives

Adjectives are words that describe nouns. By adding *-issim-*, they become SUPERlatives. They are no longer just "good" words, they're the "best!"

Positive	Superlative
nōtus well-known	**nōtissimus** very well-known/the most well-known
callidus clever	**callidissimus** very intelligent/the most intelligent
laetus happy	**laetissimus** very happy/the happiest

But, some adjectives are *irregular*: they don't like following the rules.

Positive	Superlative
bonus good	**optimus** very good/the best
malus bad	**pessimus** very bad/the worst
magnus great	**maximus** very great/the greatest

Participles

Participles are verbal adjectives. In English, these words end in "-ing" and are used to describe nouns. In Latin, these words can be identified by *-ns* and *-nt-*.

Mē bellum **gerentem** nōn spectāvistī.	You have not seen me **waging** war.
Agamemnōn aquilam hinnuleum **tenentem** vīdit.	Agamemmnon saw the eagle **holding** a fawn.
Calchās serpentem novem avēs **cōnsūmentem** vīdit.	Calchas saw the snake **eating** nine birds.

Sometimes a participle is used with a noun in the ablative case to show *when* an action occurs or *why* it occurs. This special construction is called an *ablative absolute*.

Signō vīsō, Rōmulus rēx factus est.	**After the sign was seen,** Romulus became king.
Iove volente, Priamus fīlium ad urbem retulit.	**With Jupiter willing,** Priam brought back his son to the city.
Auspiciīs relātīs, Graecī nōn iam timēbant.	**When the omens had been reported,** the Greeks were no longer afraid.

Qu-Words: Relative Pronouns and Relative Clauses

Relative clauses begin with a relative pronoun and describe a person, place, or thing. In English, relative pronouns are typically *wh*-words: "who," "whose," "which." In Latin, we use a series of *qu*-words: *quī, quae, quod.*

Imperātōrēs **quī** bonī augurēs erant bellum bene gessērunt.	The generals **who** were good augurs waged war well.
Tanaquil augur callida erat, **quae** avēs in caelō spectāvit.	Tanaquil was a clever augur, **who** watched the birds in the sky.
Aquila **quam** Tanaquil et Prīscus vīderant auspicium secundum fuerat.	The eagle **that** Tanaquil and Priscus had seen had been a favorable omen.

Infinitives

In English, infinitives typically consist of "to" followed by a verb. In Latin, they often complement or accompany certain verbs, like *volō* ("I want").

Mārcus mīles **esse** volēbat.	Marcus was wanting **to be** a soldier.
Mīlitēs Rōmānī **pugnāre** volēbant.	The Roman soldiers were wanting **to fight.**

Indirect Statement

In Latin, when we report a statement from someone other than the speaker, we use a special type of sentence. In English, these types of sentences often use the word "that."

Pullārius	**dīxit**	**deōs signum secundum dedisse.**
The chicken keeper	said	that the gods had given a favorable sign.
Pullārius	**dīxit**	**pullōs cibum cōnsūmpsisse.**
The chicken keeper	said	that the chickens had eaten the food.

Further Reading

The stories in this novella are drawn from two major ancient works, one Greek and one Roman: Homer's *Iliad* and Livy's *Ab Urbe Condita.*

In the *Iliad*—an account of the last few months of the tenth year of the Trojan War—both Greek and Trojan soldiers rely on their ability to interpret the flight patterns of birds to decide on their actions.

Agamemnon and the Eagle: Homer, *Iliad* 8.212–72

Priam and the Eagle of Jupiter: Homer, *Iliad* 24.281–348

Helenus and Hector: Homer, *Iliad* 6.72–118

Calchas and the Sparrows: Homer, *Iliad* 2.278–332

Ab Urbe Condita is an account of the history of Rome from its founding to the author's own time, during the reign of Augustus. Within the early history of Rome, there are several examples of political and military leaders relying on augury to make decisions.

Romulus and Remus: Livy, *Ab Urbe Condita* 1.3–7 (see also Cicero, *De Divinatione* 1.48)

Tarquinius and the Eagle: Livy, *Ab Urbe Condita* 1.34

Tarquinius and Attus Navius: Livy, *Ab Urbe Condita* 1.36 (see also Cicero, *De Divinatione* 1.17)

Lucius Papirius Cursor: Livy, *Ab Urbe Condita* 10.39–40

Latin-to-English Glossary

This glossary provides English definitions for all Latin words that appear in this *Encounter Latin* reader. Latin terms appear in two formats: (1) as headwords similar to those found in most standard Latin dictionaries and (2) as the inflected words (words with different endings) used throughout the book.

Inflected forms appear under their related headword and include hints about how to understand the form within the context of a Latin sentence. For example, a noun form that can function as the subject of a sentence (the person or thing that does the action of a sentence) is labeled subject. A noun form that can function as the object of a sentence (the person or thing affected by the action of a sentence) is labeled object. Verb endings in Latin can imply the subject of a sentence; inflected verbs are given with their implied subject in parentheses. For example, the verb **aedificābant** is defined as *(they) were building.*

While adjectives can have a variety of endings in Latin, their meanings do not tend to change significantly depending on the ending. Rather, adjective endings often will show which noun the adjective describes. Therefore, separate meanings are not generally given for each adjective form used in the book, although all forms that appear in the book are listed.

List of Abbreviations:

(1) = first conjugation
conj. = conjunction
f. = feminine
m. = masculine
n. = neuter

A

ā/ab, from, away from

Achilles, Achillis, *m.,* Achilles, Greek soldier
- **Achillem** (*object*)
- **Achilles** (*subject*)

ad, to, toward

adversus, -a, -um, unfavorable, adverse
- **adversa**
- **adversō**
- **adversum**

aedificō (1), build
- **aedificābant,** (they) were building
- **aedificāre,** to build
- **aedificāvit,** (he/she/it) built

Aenēās, Aenēae, *m.,* Aeneas, Trojan general
- **Aenēas** (*subject*)

Agamemnōn, Agamemnōnis, *m.,* Agamemnon, Greek general
- **Agamemmnōn** (*subject*)
- **Agamemmnōnī**, to Agamemnon

Alba Longa, Albae Longae, *f.,* ancient Latin city located in central Italy
- **Alba Longa** (*subject*)

alius, -a, -ud, other, another
- **aliī**, other (ones), others
- **aliī . . . aliī**, some . . . others
- **aliīs**, to the other (ones)

amō (1), love
- **amābam,** I was loving
- **amāre,** to love
- **amāvit,** (he/she/it) loved

amīcus, -ī, *m.,* friend
- **amīcōs,** friends (*object*)
- **ex meīs amīcīs,** of my friends

Ancus Mārcius, *m.,* fourth king of Rome
- **Ancus Mārcius** (*subject*)

annus, -ī, *m.,* year
- **annōs,** for years
- **decem annōs**, for ten years

aquila, -ae, *f.,* eagle
- **aquila,** eagle (*subject*)
- **aquilae**, of the eagle
- **aquilam**, eagle (*object*)

dē aquilā, about the eagle
Aquilōnia, -ae, *f.*, ancient city in central Italy, belonging to the Samnites
ad urbem Aquilōniam, to the city Aquilonia
Attus Navius, *m.*, augur of Tarquinius Priscus
Attum Navium (*object*)
Attus Navius (*subject*)
auctōritās, auctōritātis, *f.*, authority
auctōritātem, authority (*object*)
auctōritātemque, and authority (*object*)
audiō, audīre, audīvī, audītum, hear
audient, (they) will hear
audīre, to hear
audīverat, (he/she/it) had heard
audīvī, I heard
audīvistīne, did you hear . . . ?
audīvit, (he/she/it) heard
multīs fābulīs . . . audītīs, after many stories were heard
augur, auguris, *m.*, augur
augur, augur (*subject*)
augurem, augur (*object*)
augurēs, augurs (*subject/object*)
auguribus, for augurs
augurum, of augurs
auspicium, auspiciī, *n.*, omen
auspicia, omens, auspices (*object*)
auspiciīs . . . relātīs, when the omens had been reported
auspicium, omen (*subject/object*)
Aventīnus, -ī, *m.*, one of the seven hills of Rome
collem Aventīnum (*object*)
prope collem Aventīnum, near the Aventine Hill
avis, avis, *f.*, bird
avem, bird (*object*)
avēs, birds (*subject/object*)
avis, bird (*subject*)
avium, of birds

B

bellum, -ī, *n.*, war
bella, wars (*object*)
bellum, war (*subject/object*)
bellum gerere, to wage war
in bellīs, in wars
in bellō, in war

bene, well
bonus, -a, -um, good
  bonī
  bonum
caelum, -ī, *n.*, sky
caelum, sky (*subject/object*)
 in caelō, in the sky

C

Calchās, Calchantis, *m.*, Calchas, Greek seer and augur
  Calchās (*subject*)
  Calchantem (*object*)
callidus, -a, -um, clever
  callida
  callidī
  callidissimus, most clever, cleverest
  callidum
  callidus
  dē Rōmānīs callidīs, about clever Romans
capiō, capere, cēpī, captum, take
  capiēbant, (they) were taking
  cēperat, (he/she/it) had taken
  cēpit, (he/she/it) took
Cassandra, -ae, *f.*, Cassandra, Trojan seer and prophetess
  Cassandrae, of Cassandra
castra, castrōrum, *n.*, camp
  ad castra, to the camp
  in castrīs, in the camp
  prope castra, near the camp
cibus, -ī, *n.*, food
  cibō . . . cōnsūmptō, after the food had been eaten
  cibum, food (*object*)
Circus Maximus, *m.*, large chariot racing stadium in Rome
  Circum Maximum (*object*)
Cloāca Maxima, *f.*, the great drain of Rome's sewage system
  Cloācam Maximam (*object*)
collis, -is, *m.*, hill
  collem, hill (*object*)
  collēs, hills (*subject*)
  per collēs, through the hills
  prope collem, near the hill
  prope collēs, near the hills
cōnsūmō, cōnsūmere, cōnsūmpsī, cōnsūmptum, eat
  cōnsūmentem, eating
  cōnsūmere, to eat

cōnsūmpserant, they had eaten
cōnsūmpsisse, to have eaten
cibō . . . cōnsūmptō, after the food had been eaten
contrā, against
corōna, -ae, *f.*, crown
corōnae, to a crown
crēdō, crēdere, crēdidī, crēditum, believe
crēde, believe!
crēdēbant, (they) were believing
crēdent, they will believe
crēdidērunt, they believed
crēdidit, (he/she/it) believed
cui, to whom, for whom, whom (*see* **quī, quae, quod**)
cum, with

D

dē, about, concerning
dēfendo, dēfendere, dēfendī, dēfēnsum, defend
dēfendēbant, (they) were defending
dēfendēbās, you were defending
dēfendēbat, (he/she/it) was defending
dēfendere, to defend
dēfendērunt, (they) defended
dēfendisse, to have defended
dēfendunt, (they) defend
deinde, then
deus, -ī, *m.*, god
deī, gods (*subject*)
deōrum, of the gods
deōs, gods (*object*)
dīs volentibus, with the gods willing
dexter, dextra, dextrum, right
ā dextrā parte, from the right side
dīcō, dīcere, dīxī, dīctum, say
dīcēbant, they were saying
difficilis, -e, difficult
difficile
difficillimum, most difficult
dīcō, dīcere, dīxī, dīctum, say
dīxistī, you said
dīxit, (he/she/it) said
dō, dare, dedī, datum, give
dābant, (they) were giving
dābō, I will give
dare, to give
date, give!

dedērunt, (they) gave
dedisse, to have given
dedistis, you all gave
dedit, (he/she/it) gave
dō, I give
duo, duae, duo, two
duo
duōs
duodecim, twelve

E

ē/ex, out of, of, from
ego, meī, mihi, mē, mē, I, me
ego, I (*subject*)
mihi, to me, for me
mē, me (*object*)
eī, to him, for him (*see* **is, ea, id**)
eīs, to them, for them (*see* **is, ea, id**)
eius, his, her, its (*see* **is, ea, id**)
eōs, them (*see,* **is, ea, id)**
eram, I was (*see* **sum**)
erant, (they) were (*see* **sum**)
erat, (he/she/it) was (*see* **sum**)
eris, you will be (*see* **sum**)
erit, (he/she/it) will be (*see* **sum**)
erō, I will be (*see* **sum**)
es, you are (*see* **sum**)
esse, to be (*see* **sum**)
esset, (he/she/it) was (*see* **sum**)
est, (he/she/it) is (*see* **sum**)
estne, is he/she/it . . .? (*see* **sum**)
et, and
et . . . et, both . . . and
Ētrūscus, -a, -um, Etruscan, related to the ancient people of Etruria
Ētrūscus
eum, him (*object*) (*see* **is, ea, id**)

F

fābula, -ae, *f.*, story
fābulae, stories (*subject*)
fābulam, story (*object*)
fābulās, stories (*object*)
fābulīs . . . audītīs, since they had heard many stories
in hīs fābulīs, in these stories
faciō, facere, fēcī, factum, make, do
facere, to make, do
faciēbant, they were making, doing
faciēbat, (he/she/it) was making, doing
facientēs, making
factus est, (he) became, was made
fēcērunt, (they) made, did
fēcī, I made, did

fēcit, (he/she/it) made, did
hōc factō, when this was done
familia, -ae, *f.*, family
familiam, family (*object*)
familiās, families (*object*)
fīlius, -ī, *m.*, son
fīlī, (O!) son
fīliī, sons (*subject*)
fīlium, son (*object*)
fīlius, son (*subject*)
fortis, forte, brave, strong
dē fortibus, about the brave
fortēs
fortior, braver
fortis
fortissimī, very brave, bravest
fortissimus, very brave, bravest
fortiter, bravely
frāter, frātris, *m.*, brother
frātrem, brother (*object*)
frātrēs, brothers (*subject/object*)
frātrī, to the brother
frātribus, for the brothers
fuerat, (he/she/it) had been (*see* **sum**)
fuisset, (he/she/it) had been (*see* **sum**)
futūrōs esse, (they) would be (*see* **sum**)
futūrum esset, (it) would be (*see* **sum**)

G

gerō, gerere, gessī, gestum, wage
gerēbant, (they) were waging
gerentem, waging
gerentēs, waging
gerere, to wage
gessērunt, (they) waged
gessī, I waged
gessit, (he/she/it) waged

H

habeō, habēre, habuī, habitum, have
habēbant, (they) were having
habēbat, (he/she/it) was having
habēbis, you will have
habēbō, I will have
habēmus, we have
habent, (they) have
habēre, to have
habuērunt, (they) had
habuit, (he/she/it) had
habitō, habitāre, habitāvī, habitātum, live
habitābant, (they) were living
habitāmus, we live

Hector, Hectoris, *m.,* Hector, Trojan general
  Hector (*subject*)
  Hectorem (*object*)
Helena, -ae, *f.,* wife of Greek general Menelaus, abducted by Trojan prince Paris
  Helena (*subject*)
  Helenam (*object*)
Helenus, -ī, *m.,* Helenus, Trojan soldier and augur
  Helenus (*subject*)
hic, haec, hoc, this, these
  dē hīs virīs, about these men
  haec, this, these (*subject*)
  hī, these (*subject*)
  hoc, this (*object*)
  hōc factō, when this was done
hinnuleus, -ī, *m.,* fawn, baby deer
  hinnuleum, fawn, baby deer (*object*)
Homērus, -ī, *m.,* ancient Greek author
  Homērus (*subject*)
horribilis, horribile, horrible
  horribile
hostis, -is, *m.,* enemy
  ab hostibus, from enemies
  contrā hostēs, against enemies
  hostēs, enemies (*object*)

I

iam, now
  nōn iam, no longer
Īlias, Īliadis, *f., Iliad*, an epic about the Trojan War, written by Homer
  Īliadem (*object*)
is, ea, id, this, that; he, she
  ad eōs, to them
  eī, to him, for him
  eīs, to them, for them
  eius, his, her, its
  eum, him (*object*)
  id, that (thing) (*subject/object*)
igitur, therefore
imperātor, imperātōris, *m.,* general
  dē imperātōre, about the general
  imperātor, general (*subject*)
  imperātōrem, general (*object*)
  imperātōrēs, generals (*subject/object*)
  imperātōrī, to the general
  imperātōribus, for generals

in, in
inquam, I say
inquit, (he/she/it) says, said
intellegō, intellegere, intellēxī, intellēctum, understand
  intellegēbam, I was understanding
  intellegēbant, (they) were understanding
  intellegēbat, (he/she/it) was understanding
  intellegere, to understand
  intellegisne, do you understand . . . ?
  intellegō, I understand
  intellēxērunt, (they) understood
  intellēxistī, you understood
  intellēxit, (he/she/it) understood
iter, itineris, *n.,* journey
  iter, journey (*object*)
  in itinere, on the journey
iterum, again
Iuppiter, Iovis, *m.,* Jupiter, god of the sky
  Iovem, Jupiter (*object*)
  Iove volente, with Jupiter willing
  Iovis, of Jupiter
  Iuppiter, Jupiter (*subject*)

L
laetus, -a, -um, happy
  laeta
  laetī
  laetissimī, very happy, happiest
  laetissimus, very happy, happiest
  laetus
Lūcius, -ī, *m.,* Lucius, augur and teacher of Marcus
  Lūcius (*subject*)
Lūcius Papīrius Cursor, *m.,* Roman general and consul who waged war against the Samnites
  Papīrius (*subject*)
lupus, -ī, *m.,* wolf
  ā lupīs, from wolves

M
magister, magistrī, *m.,* teacher
  magister, teacher (*subject*)
magnus, -a, -um, great
  magnam pecūniam, much money (*object*)
  magnī mōmentī, of great importance
  magnus
maximus, -a, -um, greatest, largest
  maxima

maximam
maximās
maximī mōmentī, of the greatest importance
maximum
mē, me (*object*) (*see* **egō**)
meus, -a, -um, my
ex amīcīs meīs, of my friends
meō
meum
meus
mī
mihi, to me, for me (*see* **ego**)
mīles, mīlitis, *m.,* soldier
cum mīlitibus, with soldiers
dē mīlitibus, about soldiers
mīles, soldier (*subject*)
mīlitem, soldier (*object*)
mīlitēs, soldiers (*subject/object*)
mīlitibus, to soldiers, for soldiers
mīlitis, of the soldier
mittō, mittere, mīsī, missum, send
mīsērunt, (they) sent
mīsisse, to have sent
mīsit, (he/she/it) sent
mōmentum, -ī, *n.,* importance
magnī mōmentī, of great importance
maximī mōmentī, of the greatest importance
parvī mōmentī, of little importance
morior, morī, mortuus sum, die
morī, to die
moriēbantur, (they) were dying
morīentēs, dying
moriuntur, (they) die
moriēris, (you) will die
mortuī sunt, (they) died
mortuus, -a, -um, dead
mortuum
mortuus
multus, -a, -um, much, many
cum multīs mīltibus, with many soldiers
in multīs bellīs, in many wars
multa
multās
multī
multīs fābulīs . . . audītīs, since they had heard many stories
multōs
multum

N

narrō (1), tell
  narrābat, (he/she/it) was telling
  narrāre, to tell
necō (1), kill
  necāre, to kill
  necātus est, (he) was killed
  necāvērunt, (they) killed
  necāvit, (he/she/it) killed
necesse, necessary
neque, nor, and not
  neque . . . neque, neither . . . nor
nihil, nihil, *n.*, nothing
  nihil, nothing (*subject/object*)
nōlō, nōlle, nōluī, not want
  nōlēbam, I was not wanting
  nōlēbat, (he/she/it) was not wanting
  nōlō, I do not want
nōmen, nōminis, *n.*, name
  nōmen, name (*subject/object*)
  nōmine, by name, named
nōn, not
nōs, nostrum, nōbīs, nōs, nōbīs, we, us
  nōs, we, us (*subject/object*)
noster, nostra, nostrum, our
  nostrae
  nostrī
nōtus, -a, -um, famous
  nōtī
  nōtissimī, very famous
  nōtissimum, very famous
  nōtissimus, very famous
  nōtōs
  nōtus
novem, nine
nūmen, nūminis, *n.*, divine will
  nūmen, divine will (*object*)
  nūminī, divine will (*object*)
nunc, now

O

Odyssēa, -ae, *f.*, Odyssey, an epic written by Homer about the journey of Odysseus (also known as Ulysses)
  Odyssēam (*object*)
ōlim, once, once upon a time
omnis, omne, all, every
  omnēs
  omnibus
optimus, -a, -um, best
  optimās
  optimum
  optimus
ovis, -is, *f.*, sheep
  ovēs, sheep (*object*)
  ovibus, to the sheep

P

Palātīnus, -ī, *m.*, one of the seven hills of Rome
- **collem Palātīnum,** Palatine Hill (*object*)
- **prope collem Palātinum,** near the Palatine Hill

Papīrius, *see* **Lūcius Papīrius Cursor**

pāreō, pārēre, pāruī, pāritum, obey
- **pārēbant,** (they) were obeying
- **pārent,** (they) obey
- **pārēre,** to obey
- **pāruērunt,** (they) obeyed
- **pāruit,** (he/she/it) obeyed

pars, partis, *f.*, part
- **ā dextrā parte,** from the right side
- **in quattuor partēs,** into four parts
- **in tribus partibus,** in three parts
- **pars,** part (*subject*)

parvus, -a, -um, little
- **parvī mōmentī,** of little importance

pāstor, pāstōris, *m.*, shepherd
- **duo ē pāstōribus,** two of the shepherds
- **pāstor,** shepherd (*subject*)
- **pāstōrēs,** shepherds (*subject/object*)
- **pāstōris,** of the shepherd

pater, patris, *m.*, father
- **pater,** father (*subject*)
- **patrem,** father (*object*)
- **patrēs,** fathers (*subject*)
- **patrī,** to the father

pecūnia, -ae, *f.*, money
- **pecūniam,** money (*object*)

per, through

petō, petere, petivī, petītum, seek, attack
- **petēbant,** (they) were seeking, attacking
- **petēbat,** (he/she/it) was seeking, attacking
- **petīvit,** (he/she/it) sought, attacked

pilleus, -ī, *m.*, hat
- **cum pilleō,** with the hat
- **pilleum,** hat (*object*)

populus, -ī, *m.*, people
- **prō populō Rōmānō,** for the Roman people
- **populum Rōmānum,** Roman people (*object*)

porcus, -ī, *m.*, pig
- **porcōs,** pigs (*object*)
- **porcum,** pig (*object*)
- **porcus,** pig (*subject*)

possum, posse, potuī, be able
- **possum,** I am able
- **possumus,** we are able

possunt, (they) are able
poterant, (they) were able
poterat, (he/she/it) was able
potes, you are able
potuit, (he/she/it) was able
postquam, after
potestās, potestātis, *f.*, power
potestātem, power (*object*)
prīmus, -a, -um, first
prīmum, first(ly)
prīmus
Prīscus, *see* **Tarquinius Prīscus**
prō, for, on behalf of
prope, near
pūblicus, -a, -um, public
rem pūblicam, the republic, the public business (*object*)
pugnō (1), fight
pugnābant, (they) were fighting
pugnābat, (he/she/it) was fighting
pugnābunt, (they) will fight
pugnant, (they) fight
pugnantem, fighting
pugnāre, to fight
pugnāverat, (he/she/it) had fought
pugnāvērunt, (they) fought
pugnāvimus, we fought
pugnāvit, (he/she/it) fought
pullārius, -ī, *m.*, chicken keeper
pullāriī, chicken keepers (*subject*)
pullārium, chicken keeper (*object*)
pullārius, chicken keeper (*subject*)
pullus, -ī, (sacred) chicken
pullī, chickens (*subject*)
pullīs, to the chickens, for the chickens
pullōrum, of the chickens
pullōs, chickens (*object*)

Q

quam, *conj.*, than (*for the relative pronoun, see* **quī**)
quamquam, although
quī, quae, quod, who, which, that
cui, to whom, for whom, whom
in quā, in which
in quibus, in which
quae, who (*subject*)

quam, whom, which (*object*)
quī, who, which (*subject*)
quod, which, that (*object*)
quōrum, whose, of whom, of which
quōs, which (*object*)

quia, because
quid, what (*subject*)
quis, who (*subject*)
quod, *conj.*, because (*for the relative pronoun, see* **quī**)
quoque, also

R

rectē, correctly
referō, referre, retulī, relātum, report, bring back
auspiciīs relātīs, when the omens had been reported
referēbat, (he/she/it) was reporting
referunt, (they) report
referre, to report,
refers, you report,
refert, (he/she/it) reports
retulerat, (he/she/it) had reported
retulit, (he/she/it) reported, brought back

Remora, -ae, *f.*, Remus's proposed name for the city that would become Rome
Remoram (*object*)

Remus, -ī, *m.*, Remus, twin brother of Romulus
Remus (*subject*)
Remum (*object*)

rēs, reī, *f.*, business
rem pūblicam, the republic, the public business (*object*)

respondeō, respondēre, respondī, respōnsum, respond
respondeō, I respond
respondet, (he/she/it) responds

rēx, rēgis, *m.*, king
rēgem, king (*object*)
rēgēs, kings (*subject*)
rēgī, to the king
rēgis, of the king
rēx, king (*subject*)

Rōma, -ae, *f.*, city of Rome, capital of the Roman Empire
Rōma (*subject*)
Rōmam (*object*)

Rōmulus, -ī, *m.*, Romulus, first king of Rome
Rōmulus (*subject*)
Rōmulum (*object*)

S

Samnīs, Samnītis, *m.,* Samnite, a member of the confederation of tribes in south-central Italy
- **Samnītēs** (*subject*)
- **contrā Samnītēs,** against the Samnites

sciō, scīre, scīvī, scītum, know
- **sciēbant,** (they) were knowing
- **sciēbat,** (he/she/it) was knowing
- **sciō,** I know
- **scīre,** to know
- **sciunt,** (they) know
- **scīvī,** I knew
- **scīvit,** (he/she/it) knew
- **scīvērunt,** (they) knew

sē, he

secundus, -a, -um, favorable
- **secundiōrem,** more favorable
- **secundum**

sed, but

serpēns, serpentis, *m./f.,* snake
- **serpēns,** snake (*subject*)
- **serpentem,** snake (*object*)

sex, six

signum, -ī, *n.,* sign
- **signa,** signs (*object*)
- **signō vīsō,** after the sign was seen
- **signum,** sign (*object*)

similis, simile, similar
- **similem**
- **similēs**
- **similis**

spectō (1), watch
- **spectābant,** (they) were watching
- **spectābat,** (he/she/it) was watching
- **spectantem,** watching
- **spectāre,** to watch
- **spectāvērunt,** (they) watched
- **spectāvī,** I watched
- **spectāvimus,** we watched
- **spectāvistī,** you watched
- **spectāvit,** (he/she/it) watched
- **Trōiānīs spectantibus,** while the Trojans were watching

subitō, suddenly

sum, esse, fuī, to be
- **eram,** I was
- **erant,** (they) were
- **erat,** (he/she/it) was
- **eris,** you will be
- **erit,** (he/she/it) will be
- **erō,** I will be
- **es,** you are
- **esse,** to be
- **esset,** it was
- **est,** (he/she/it) is

estne, is he/she/it . . .?
fuerat, (he/she/it) had been
fuisset, (he/she/it) had been
futūrōs esse, (they) would be
futūrum esset, (it) would be
sunt, (they) are, there are
suus, -a, -um, his own, her own, its own, their own
suam, their own
suās, their own
suum, his own

T
tamen, nevertheless
Tanaquil, Tanaquīlis, *f.*, augur and wife of Tarquinius Priscus, fifth king of Rome
Tanaquil (*subject*)
Tarquinius Prīscus, *m.*, fifth king of Rome
ad Prīscum, to Priscus
Prīscus (*subject*)
Prīscum (*object*)
Tarquinius (*subject*)
tē, you (*object*) (*see* **tū**)
teneō, tenēre, tenuī, hold
tenēns, holding
tenentem, holding
tenēre, to hold
tenuērunt, (they) held
tenuit, (he/she/it) held
tibi, for you (*see* **tū**)
timeō, timēre, timuī, fear
timēbant, (they) were fearing
timēbat, (he/she/it) was afraid
timēns, fearing
timeō, I fear
timuit, (he/she/it) feared
trēs, tria, three
in tribus partibus, in three parts
tū, tuī, tibi, tē, tē, you
tē, you (*object*)
tibi, for you
tū, you (*subject*)
tuus, -a, -um, your
tuam
tuōs
tuum

U
ubi, when, where
Ulixēs, Ulixis, *m.*, Ulysses (otherwise known as Odysseus), Greek general
Ulixēs (*subject*)
Ulixī, to Ulysses
urbs, -is, *f.*, city
in urbe, in the city
urbem, city (*object*)

urbī, to the city
urbs, city (*subject*)
ūva, -ae, *f.*, grape
ūvās, grapes (*object*)
uxor, uxōris, *f.*, wife
cum uxōre, with his wife
uxor, wife (*subject*)

V

velle, to want (*see* **volō, velle**)
victor, victōris, *m.*, victor
victor, victor (*subject*)
victōrem, victor (*object*)
victōrēs, victors (*subject*)
videō, vidēre, vīdī, vīsum, see
signō vīsō, after the sign was seen
vīderant, (they) had seen
vīderat, (he/she/it) had seen
vidēre, to see
vīdī, I saw
vīdit, (he/she/it) saw
vīnetum, -ī, *n.*, vineyard
in vīnētō, in the vineyard
vīnētum, vineyard (*subject*)
vir, -ī, *m.*, man, husband
dē virīs, about men
vir, man (*subject*)
virī, men (*subject*)
virō, man
virōs, men (*object*)
virum, man, husband (*object*)
vīs, you want (*see* **volō, velle**)
vōbis, to you all (*see* **vōs**)
volō (1), fly
volābant, (they) were flying
volāns, flying
volantem, flying
volantēs, flying
volāvērunt, (they) flew
volāvit, (he/she/it) flew
volō, velle, voluī, want
dīs volentibus, with the gods willing
Iove volente, with Jupiter willing
velle, to want
vīs, you want
volēbam, I was wanting
volēbant, (they) were wanting
volēbat, (he/she/it) was wanting
volō, I want
voluerat, (he/she/it) had wanted
voluērunt, (they) wanted
voluit, (he/she/it) wanted
vōs, vestrum, vōbīs, vōs, vōbīs, you all
vōbīs, to you all
vultur, vulturis, *m.*, vulture
vulturēs, vultures (*object*)

PGIL2021USA